BORN INTO A PANDEMIC...
A Mother's Precious Gift

By Dr. Candace White
Recognized by ESSENCE Magazine as an "Essential Hero"

Illustrated by: Ministry Event Marketing

Born into a Pandemic... A Mother's Precious Gift by Dr. Candace White

Published by Ministry Event Marketing
400 N Ashley Dr. Suite 1900 Tampa, FL 33602
www.ministryeventmarketing.com

For permissions contact:

info@drcandacewhite.com or www.drcandacewhite.com

Illustrated by Ministry Event Marketing

ISBN: 978-0-9991012-2-3

Acknowledgements

This book is dedicated to expectant mothers and mothers who gave birth during the pandemic. As well as, the women, men, and children in the world who celebrated the arrival of new life during these unprecedented times.

This book is also dedicated to my Husband - Terry, Son - Solomon, Daughter - Onar, Parents - Albert and Ora, Siblings - Bridgette and Marcus, Nephews - DeLarse IV and Baylon, Niece - Kinnidie, Cousins - Nickki, Monique, Donjhae, and Kylan. My God sisters - Latracia and Delacia, God daughters - Lauren, Hannah, and Tomecia.

This book is in honor of my Grandparents, the late Elmer and Altameze Henry and James and Ella Mae Driskell.

BORN INTO A PANDEMIC

A Mother's Precious Gift

By Dr. Candace White

Recognized by ESSENCE Magazine as an "Essential Hero"

Illustrated by: Ministry Event Marketing

You were born in my dreams,
before I knew that you would be...

God gave me a precious gift,
a beautiful baby, that would be
birthed by me.

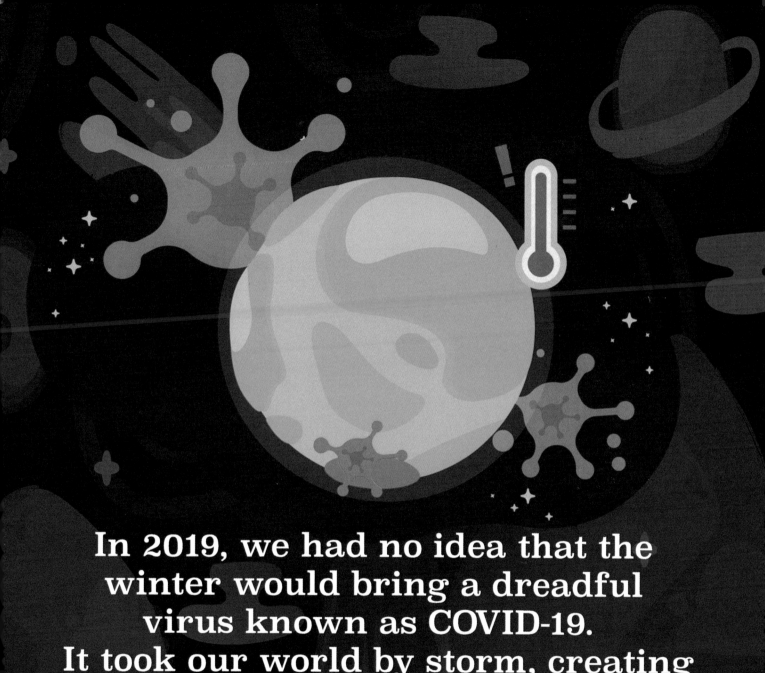

In 2019, we had no idea that the winter would bring a dreadful virus known as COVID-19.
It took our world by storm, creating what many feared would soon become the new norm.

As you grew within my womb,
I covered you in prayer each day.

I prayed that God would protect you
and help keep my fears away.

As time progressed and my belly grew,
who knew that a pandemic would
then ensue.

Many unknowns for moms and dads
to be...would our babies need to live in
a bubble to be COVID-19 free?

Visits to the doctor's office would no longer look the same.
The appointments may be virtual...

Or in a parking lot, just the same.

The waiting rooms are now empty,
seating is six feet apart.
Social distancing will help to keep us safe.
Remember these tips and be smart!

Stop the Spread
HEALTH TIP

Make sure your mask covers your nose and mouth!
DO NOT WEAR YOUR MASK BELOW YOUR CHIN OR NOSE.

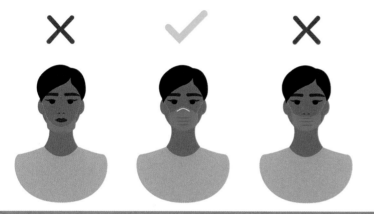

HEALTH TIP

Sing your ABC's all the way down to Z or
count from 1-20 when washing your hands.
This will help to get rid of the germs!

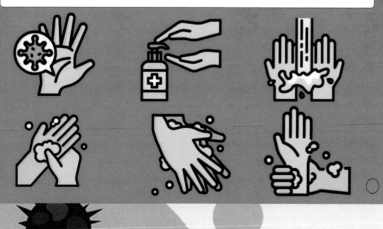

Oh, don't forget
your mask and
sanitizer in hand.

We must not
spread these germs,
that's how the
pandemic began.

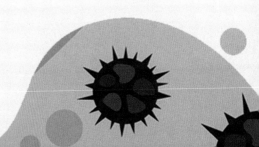

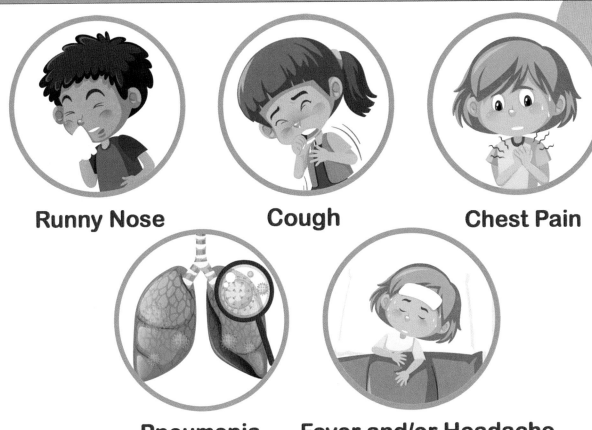

Runny Nose   **Cough**   **Chest Pain**

Pneumonia   **Fever and/or Headache**

"Do you have a fever, cough, sore throat,
loss of smell or taste?"
These were the questions asked
to screen us case by case.

The day I went into labor,

I labored at home for as long as I could.

The fear of contracting the virus weighed

heavily on my motherhood.

Loved ones were not allowed in the delivery room, only one would have to do.

But I knew that we would get through this because that is what mothers do.

ATTENTION:
LIMITED VISITATION ALERT

To help protect our patients, providers, employees and the community, the following visitation guidelines are in effect:

 COVID-19 Screening

 One WELL Visitor Per Day

 Additional Guests Should Remain At Home

When the doctor said, "Push!" I knew the time had finally arrived to bring you into this uncertain world to live and to thrive.

Your Grandparents, close family, and friends were not even allowed in the waiting room.

We had to celebrate your arrival via video chats and over Zoom.

The day we left the hospital, you were our precious blessing in hand.

God kept you safe in his arms. That was a part of His plan.

How will we get through this? What are we to do? The answer lies with the Almighty. God's grace will carry us through.

Fear not, for I am with you; be not dismayed, for I am your God; I will strengthen you, I will help you, I will uphold you with my righteous right hand. Isaiah 41:10

We were overjoyed to have you home,
but unsure of what we would now do.
Will we take walks in the park
wearing masks and dressed in hazmat suits?

Will birthdays now be celebrated without the presence of family and friends?

With no contact, drive by parties, and drop off stations for gifts?

Will schools reopen to the public or
will homeschooling become the new norm?
Will graduations take place virtually
until we weather the pandemic storm?

Whether the virus stays or goes,
this we do not know.
Hopefully, the vaccine will provide a cure
or possibly an antidote.

Although the future is unknown,
there is one thing that remains true.
God's love is everlasting and
He will see us through.
So don't give up or get discouraged,
we must not give in.
Remember, we are all in this together.
And together, we shall win!

For God so loved the world, that he gave his only Son,
that whoever believes in him should not
perish but have eternal life. John 3:16

The End...

Dear Reader,

Thank you for supporting this project and for taking this journey with me. This keepsake treasure will be around for you to enjoy now and for years to come.

As you embark upon your path towards motherhood, please use the following pages in this book to capture some of your own precious moments.

These pages are intended to encourage you to maintain good overall health and wellness during these unprecedented times of the global COVID-19 pandemic.

Let's stay connected, blessings,

Dr. Candace White

You can follow me:

@therealdrcandacewhite

@therealdrcandacewhite

@DrCandaceWhite

BORN DURING A PANDEMIC

Introducing My Coronial

Baby name: _____

Birth weight: _____

Height: _____

Date of birth: _____

Place of birth: _____

Time of birth: _____

Mother's name:_____**Age:**_____

Father's name:_____**Age:**_____

What helped you get through your pregnancy during the pandemic?

_____
_____
_____
_____
_____
_____
_____
_____
_____
_____

Mom & Baby

3 SURViVAL TiPS FOR MOMS DURiNG THE PANDEMiC:

1. Give Yourself Grace

Carrying life during a pandemic has added additional challenges and stressors. If you have gotten off track, i.e., adhering to a healthy diet, exercise, or preserving your mental health, know that there is always tomorrow. Start anew by forgiving yourself or any lapses in judgment. Add in some extra self-love and give yourself compassion. You are amazing, beautiful, and have been blessed with the precious gift of life.

2. Focus on what you can control

Although we can't control when this pandemic will end, we can control some of our behaviors and what goes on in our daily lives. We can start with prioritizing our health and being compliant with our doctor's appointments - practice self-care. Continue to mask up in public places, social distance, and wash your hands. Eat a balanced diet full of fresh vegetables and fruit. Drink plenty of water, get exercise, and at least 8 hours of sleep at night.

3. Your feelings are important! DO NOT IGNORE THEM!

If you begin to feel like stress, feelings of sadness, and/or anxiety are beginning to affect your ability to function or carry out your daily activities of living, do not be afraid to ask for help. Anytime you have a thought that does not make you feel good, switch to an idea or belief that leaves you feeling more empowered. Writing in a journal can be a great way to air out your emotions and feelings. The mind, body, and spirit are all connected. To achieve a balance between the three, you must think positively, live moderately, and nurture the soul.

HEALTH TIP:

Develop a daily routine of using positive affirmations throughout your pregnancy. This helps encourage a healthy mindset and build confidence about your current state of pregnancy while significantly reducing stress and anxiety. Repeating positive affirmations can rewire the brain and strengthen brain areas that stimulate positive feelings.

Positive Affirmations

I am blessed to be carrying the precious gift of life.

I look forward to a happy, healthy pregnancy.

I am learning to transform my fears into faith.

I welcome the changes in my body.

I embrace the good days, the challenging days,
and choose to enjoy each moment along this journey.

I will use my voice to express my feelings
and create healthy boundaries.

I believe my body is capable and ready to allow a
peaceful and effortless birthing experience to take place.

I am brave, tenacious, confident, and faithful.

God will carry me through this pregnancy.

Write your positive affirmations here:

I am _____

I am _____

I am _____

I am _____

I am _____

I am _____

I am _____

I am _____

About The Author

Dr. Candace White is a board-certified primary care physician, public health leader, and patient advocate who serves the greater Atlanta, GA area.

She works on the frontline to serve her community and patients alike. Her mission is to improve her patient's quality of life through continuity of care, education, and empowerment.

She worked throughout her entire pregnancy, enduring multiple COVID-19 exposures, unknowingly at the time. Prayerfully, she remained COVID-19 free and delivered a healthy baby girl at the height of the pandemic on April 10, 2020. She was recognized by ESSENCE magazine as an Essential Hero and was awarded the Amazing Grace Award for her service to her patients and community. She is now fully vaccinated with Pfizer/BioNtech's COVID-19 vaccine.

Made in the USA
Columbia, SC
16 February 2022

56361925R00020